My Alphabet Chart

The Alphabet Chart

This chart will help the child to connect lower-case letters with capital letters. Help the child to cut it
out and colour it in. This is fun to do and will help the child to remember the pictures that go with each letter.
Also, use this chart for reference when completing the activities on pages 30 and 31.

My Alphabet Chart

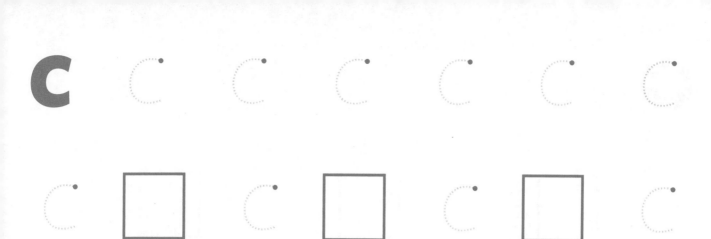

C c · c · c · c · c · c · c ·

c · ☐ c · ☐ c · ☐ c ·

cat

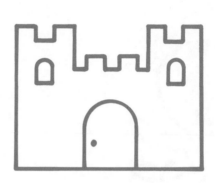

castle

carrot

car

caterpillar

cup

How to describe forming the letter:
c – pencil on the big dot, join up the little dots – 'c'
In the boxes, practise writing the letter shape without the help of the dots.

pages 5 to 10: Letters in these pages all start with a 'c' shape.
Note: There is no activity for 'q'.

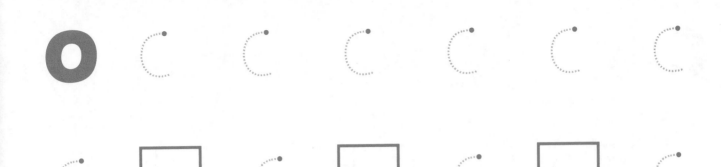

o

octopus

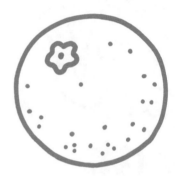

orange

ostrich

How to describe forming the letter:
o – pencil on the big dot, join up the little dots, then go all the way round – 'o'
In the boxes, practise writing the letter shape without the help of the dots.

apple

ant

axe

anchor

How to describe forming the letter:
a – pencil on the big dot, join up the little dots, little stick up and back down and flick – 'a'
In the boxes, practise writing the letter shape without the help of the dots.

d c c c c c c c

c c c c

dog

dice

door

duck

domino

g c c c c c c c c c c c

c c c c c c c

gate

goat

guitar

gorilla

garden

How to describe forming the letter:
g – pencil on the big dot, join up the little dots, little stick up, a long stick back down and curl under – 'g'
In the boxes, practise writing the letter shape without the help of the dots.

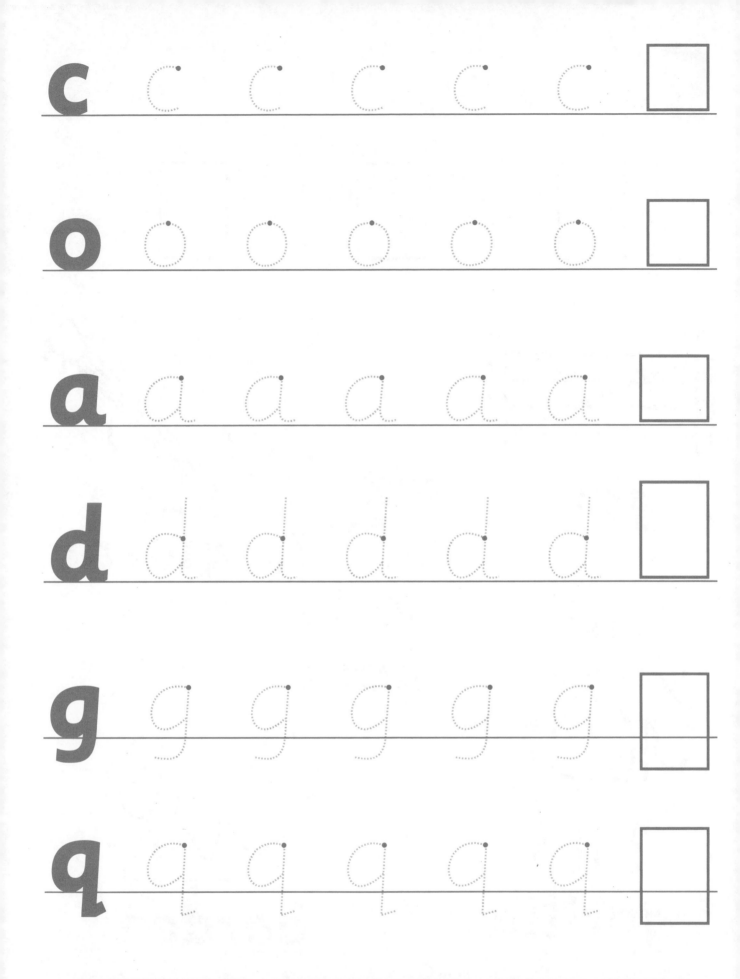

c c c c c c □

o o o o o o □

a a a a a a □

d d d d d d □

g g g g g g □

q q q q q q □

Ask the child to practise writing each letter shape by starting at the big dot and joining up the little dots.
Always start with the 'c' shape. In the boxes, practise writing the letter shapes without the help of the dots.

r

rabbit

rainbow

ring

rocket

How to describe forming the letter:
Note: 'r' has a little stick down
r – pencil on the big dot, join up the little dots, go back up and over – 'r'
In the boxes, practise writing the letter shape without the help of the dots.

pages 11 to 17: Letters in these pages all start with a downward stroke then go back up.

n

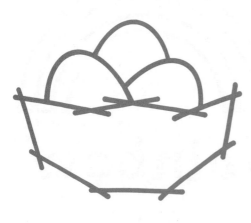

nest

nurse

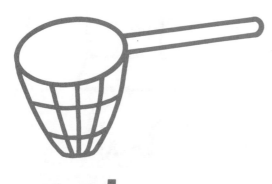

net

needle

How to describe forming the letter:
Note: 'n' has a little stick down
n – pencil on the big dot, join up the little dots, go back up and over and down and flick – 'n'
In the boxes, practise writing the letter shape without the help of the dots.

m

mouse

moon

monkey

mop

How to describe forming the letter:
Note: 'm' has a little stick down
m – pencil on the big dot, join up the little dots, go back up and over and down, then again go back up
and over and down, and flick – 'm'
In the boxes, practise writing the letter shape without the help of the dots.

h

house

hedgehog

hat

helicopter

How to describe forming the letter:
Note: 'h' has a big stick down
h – pencil on the big dot, join up the little dots, go halfway back up and over and down, and flick – 'h'
In the boxes, practise writing the letter shape without the help of the dots.

b

ball

bed

banana

bus

bee

15

p

panda

pear

parachute

purse

r r r r r r r ☐

n n n n n n n ☐

m m m m m m m ☐

h h h h h h h ☐

b b b b b b ☐

p p p p p p p ☐

Ask the child to practise writing each letter shape by starting at the big dot and joining up the little dots.
Start with a downward stroke.
In the boxes, practise writing the letter shapes without the help of the dots.

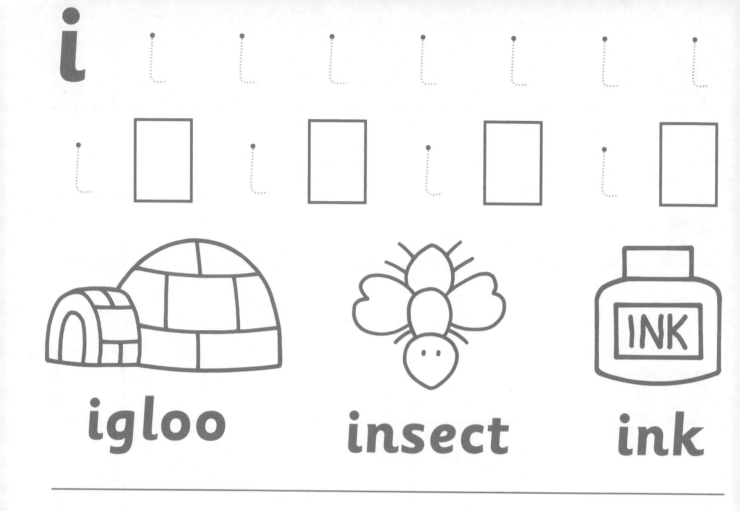

igloo

insect

ink

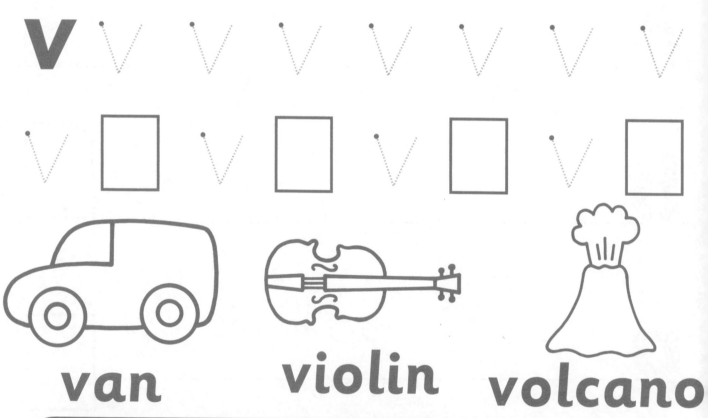

van

violin

volcano

How to describe forming the letters:
Note: 'i' has a little stick down / 'v' has a sloping stick down
i – pencil on the big dot, join up the little dots, and flick. Put a dot above – 'i'
v – pencil on the big dot, join up the little dots, sloping down and up – 'v'
In the boxes, practise writing the letter shapes without the help of the dots.

pages 18 to 24: Letters in these pages all start with a downward stroke.
Note: There is no activity for 'x' as there are not enough suitable matching pictures.

jug

jigsaw

jelly

jam

How to describe forming the letter:

Note: 'j' has a long stick down.

j – pencil on the big dot, join up the little dots and curl under. Put a dot above – 'j'

In the boxes, practise writing the letter shape without the help of the dots.

l

ladybird

ladder

lamp

lion

lorry

How to describe forming the letter:
Note: 'l' has a big stick down
l – pencil on the big dot, join up the little dots, and flick – 'l'
In the boxes, practise writing the letter shape without the help of the dots.

t

tortoise

table

tent

tiger

teapot

k

kite

kettle

king

kangaroo

key

How to describe forming the letter:
Note: 'k' has a big stick down
k – pencil on the big dot, join up the little dots. Put one leg kicking up and one leg kicking down, and flick – 'k'. In the boxes, practise writing the letter shape without the help of the dots.

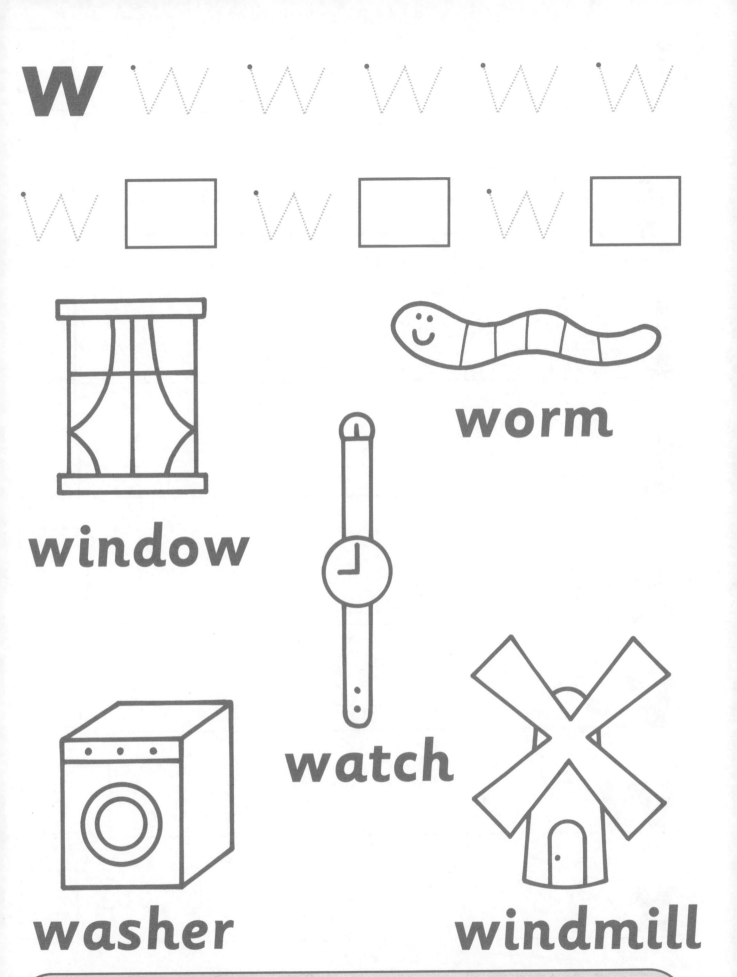

window

worm

watch

washer

windmill

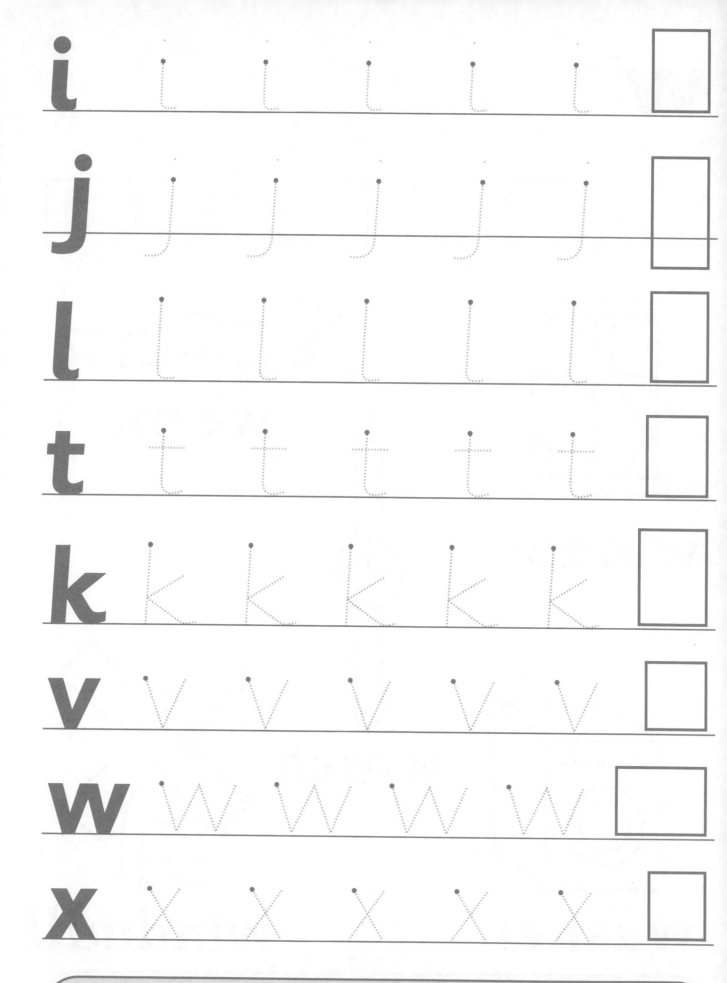

Ask the child to practise writing each letter shape by starting with the big dot and joining up the little dots.
Start with a downward stroke for **i, j, l, t, k**. Start with a sloping stroke down for **v, w, x**.
In the boxes, practise writing the letter shapes without the help of the dots.

e

elephant

egg

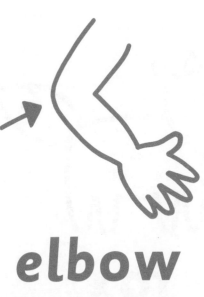

egg cup

elbow

How to describe forming the letter:

e – pencil on the big dot, join up the little dots and curl round – 'e'

In the boxes, practise writing the letter shape without the help of the dots.

pages 25 to 29: These pages contain the remaining letters.

f

fish

fork

fan

fox

face

How to describe forming the letter:
Note: 'f' has a big stick down
f – pencil on the big dot, join up the little dots. Put a little line halfway up – 'f'
In the boxes, practise writing the letter shape without the help of the dots.

s

s s s s s s s s s s s

s □ s □ s □ s □ s □

sun

seal

sock

sandwich

see-saw

How to describe forming the letter:
s – pencil on the big dot, join up the little dots, curling one way and then the other way – 's'
In the boxes, practise writing the letter shape without the help of the dots.

u

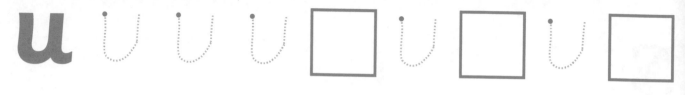

umbrella

y

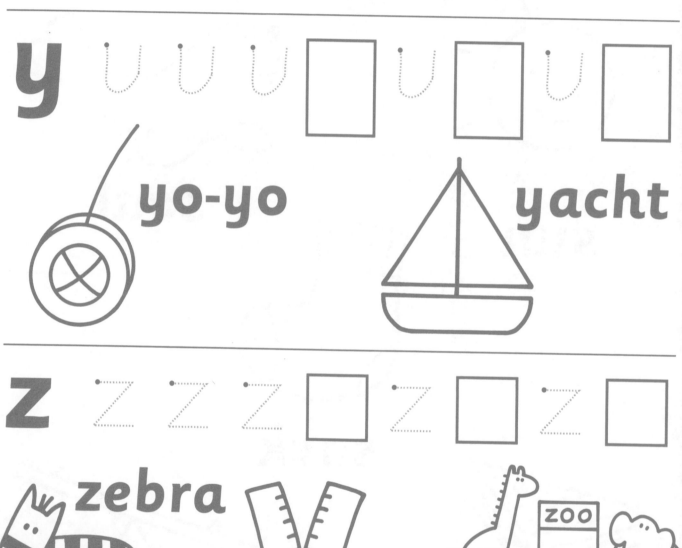

yo-yo

yacht

z

zebra

zip

zoo

e e e e e e □

f f f f f f □

s s s s s s □

u u u u u u □

y y y y y y □

z z z z z z □

Ask the child to practise writing each letter shape by starting at the big dot and joining up the little dots. In the boxes, practise writing the letter shapes without the help of the dots.

a   D

b   C

c   F

d   A

e   B

f   E

g   I

h   J

i   G

j   M

k   H

l   K

m   L

pages 30 and 31
Ask the child to draw a line to join the lower-case letter to the capital letter. Now join the capital letter to the correct picture. Use the chart from page 3 to help.